C000202128

ILLUSTRATED BY
WOODY

Macmillan Children's Books CARDINAL NEWMAN SCHOOL

LIBRARY

First published 1995 by
Macmillan Children's Books
a Division of Macmillan Publishers Ltd
25 Eccleston Place, London SW1W 9NF
and Basingstoke

Associated companies throughout the world

ISBN 0 330 33875 7

9 8 7 6 5 4 3 2

A CIP catalogue record for this book is available from
the British Library.

Typeset in 12/14 Monophoto Gill Sans
Printed by Mackays of Chatham plc, Chatham, Kent

CONTENTS

Matt

Wes

Pete

An Alphabetic . . .
(fill in the spaces!)

A is a triangle with legs, is a tepee, is a rocket's nose.

B is a three with a propeller, a butterfly with its wings folded, is a bit of a hot cross bun.

C is nearly nothing at

D

E

F

G

H

I

J

K

L

M
N
O
P
Q
R
S
T
U
V
W

X is a trestle, crossed swords, two Vs kissing.

Y is a cocktail, a boat with its anchor down, coffee filtering.

Z is a duck by Picasso.

Out of the Cup

An open goal, lad, a gaping, can't-miss goal!
A banged-in, dead-cert, asking-for-it goal!
Talk about butter-fingers – we'll have to call you
butter-boots! What d'you do? Smear Kerrygold on them?

All you had to do was tap it in; a simple tap,
a toe-cap tap. But no! you had to dash at it,
to rush at it, to take a mighty swipe at it.
I'm not the only one, the only one

who wished to hear a solid thud, a spot-on thud,
dead-centre-of-the-ball and cheer-your-lungs-out,
go-down-in-history, kick-of-the-century thud.

A goal! a know-you've-won, a blinder goal. And NOT
a try-again-next-season shot.

Football Mad

Gizza go of yer footie,
Just one belt of the ball?
Lend yer me scarf on Satdee
for just one boot at the wall?

Give yer a poster of Gazza
for one tiny kick with my right?
Do y'after be that mingey?
Go on, don't be tight!

A chest-it-down to me left foot,
a touch, a header, a dribble?
A shot between the goalie's legs,
a pass right down the middle?

Y'can borree me Madonna records
for as long as ever y'like,
I'll give yer a go around the block
on me brandnew mountain bike.

One day I'll be playing for Liverpule
Wen youze are all forgot.
Go on, a titchy kick of yer footie,
one meezly penulty shot?

I'll get yer a season ticket
when I am in The Team,
and wen I'm scorin' in the Cup
you'd be sittin' by the Queen.

A Dog's Life

I don't like being me sometimes,
        slumped here
on the carpet, cocking my ears
        every time
someone shuffles or shifts their feet,
        thinking
could be going walkies or getting grub
        or allowed to see
if the cat's left more than a smell
        on her plate.
She's never refused, that cat! Sometimes
        I find myself
dreaming, (twitching my eyes, my fur)
        of being just
say *half* as canny as her, with her pert miaow,
        her cheeky tail
flaunting! These people sprawled
        in armchairs
gawping at telly, why don't they play ball
        with me
or enjoy a good nose-licking, eh?

Cat and Mouse

Skitterings in the shrubbery,
trembling, twitching leaves.

Cat in shadow. Cat on the lawn.
Still as brick, intent as the moon.

A pounce, a crash!

Enter Cat with mouse-moustache!

Still Awake

Dogs booming like guns
in the echoing yards;
cats rattling bins
and squalling over scraps;
the gate unlatched
creaking its hinges;
a faulty street lamp blinking
orange, orange; high heels
on pavements; a drunk crooning
a loud love song;
smells of fish and chips.

Walking a Friend's Dog
– Devon Midnight

I just can't see,
don't know
where anything is.

I must *imagine* hedges,
the sky, the lane ahead.
Tonight is as black
as loudspeakers,
as peppercorns, as rain-
soaked soil, as black
as a mole's eyesight
underground.

It doesn't bother the dog.
He can see with his wet
black nose, snuffling
at hedges. He can tell
where a fox has shouldered
through, can hear
the fieldmice scratch.

Tonight is black
as lofts, as cupboards
under stairs, so dark
I'm scared . . .

me . . . a grown man
from the phosphorescent city . . .
asking *'Is it time to turn back home?
Are you still there?'*

Rhinoceros

God simply got bored and started doodling
with ideas he'd given up on, scooping off the floor
bits and bobs and sticking them together:
the tail of a ten-ton pig he'd meant for Norway
the long skull of a too-heavy dinosaur,
the armour plating of his first version of
the hippo, an unpainted beak of a toucan
stuck on back to front, a dash of tantrums
he intended for the Abyssinian owl, the same
awful grey colour he'd used for landscaping the moon.

And tempted to try it with the batteries,
he set it down on the wild plains of Africa,
grinned at what he saw and let it run.

Water Haiku

Electric thunder
in the hills. I wash my hands,
my face with lightning.

This gush, this splatter
from the hose may once have been
gulped in by a whale.

Autumn Gale

A Dickens of a day! You can't tell leaves
from birds — panicky things
hurtling past windows. Everything's
having a rough time. Hedges shivering
with fright: that plastic bag
tugging to free itself from the barbs
of the blackthorn, this back-garden willow
taking such stick it's nearly thrashed
out of its wits. Some big bully
is terrorizing the neighbourhood,
huffing and puffing to blow your house down.

In Bed

Sleep like a top?

Where did you get
that expression from, eh?
And just how is it done?

Sounds far too dizzying
for me . . . wobble . . . wobble
we all fall down!

Is it anything like
sleeping *tight?*
My old man after a few pints!

No,
I'd rather sleep
like . . . like . . . a big
old fashioned
sideboard,   solidly, comfortably
                             here
                             all night . . . all right?

The Coming of the Vandals

A thud at the window makes me jump
out of a CD Mozart trance!

A bird has clunked its hapless skull
on glass? Not with curtains drawn
at night! My wife has forgotten her keys,
has chucked a clod of grass to stir me,
serves me right?

The street is empty, perfectly still,
its silence slaps me in the mouth.

Who? What? Why? There's no one there!

But just look at this hole in the pane
the size of a fist, like the ghost of a spider
in a cobweb of cracks.

Who hates music that much and who hates me
because of it? Or is it something more frightening,
more mindless than that?

I only know the spell of music's snapped, the night
is dangerous, the house itself's afraid.

The Other Night

We were playing *Coronation Street*
the other night . . . and . . . well
I was Des the bookie
and she was that Racquel.

She smelt all talc and pink soap.
Her hair was soft as down;
she told me I was handsome,
best-looking guy in town!

We stood beneath the lamp post
eating fish and chips.
O my salt-and-vinegar Racquel!
I kissed her on the lips!

Telling

Eh, mum! You're rotten!
Why did you have to tell?
Now grandad's a smirking idiot
And grandma's grinning as well.

Our Hannah is all sniggers:
Why does she have to know?
It'll be round the school tomorrow:
I've decided not to go!

Anyway who was it told you?
Bet it was Ronnie Wall's mam!
Just you wait till I see him,
He'll be like strawberry jam!

And why'd you say it so smarmy?
Why did you lay it on thick?
'Our Michael's got a girlfriend!'
You made me feel quite sick.

Dad's been at me all evening,
Acting the stupid goat
With his: 'Tell us her name then, Michael,
And I'll give you this £5 note!'

I'm not telling anyone:
It would not be fair.
No one's getting it out of me,
It's private, see! So there!

Enter the Hero

'Were you born in a field?'
my mother yelled
as I left the door ajar.

'Put the wood in the hole!'
my old man growled
through a mouth like a gangster's scar.

But didn't they say
that I'd been found
under a cabbage or goosegog tree?
squidgy like a little worm,
as tall as a grasshopper's knee?

And because I look a bit of a scruff,
not like a brandnew pin,
they say that I am something
the dog has just dragged in!

Some days, some days, some days,
you know you just can't win!

Don't Argue

Over there! The whatsit!
The oo-jimmy-flip! You know!
The thingee! Near the oojah!
where the what-d'y-call'm go!

Are you deaf or daft? The thingummybob!
The doobree! Can't you hear?
The whatsisname, the whatever-it-is!
JUST BRING IT OVER HERE!

Down with Flu!

I've a bag code,
fluey and flemmy
in me node;

feel like somebobby's
stuffed
a hod wet towel
insibe
me achin' heb;

I've a scratchy frob
in me throbe,
me chest's full
ob frobspawn;

I wheeze and explose
ashoo-ashoo-ashoo
into me hankersneeze,
I tishoo-tishoo-tishoo
into me tishoo;

I've a bag code
in me node,
and I'm feb up,
really feb up,

really, really, really
feb up here in beb.

One Spring Day

Melanie, Melanie Wilberforce
Knows just how it feels
To clatter on the garden path
In her mam's high heels.

Baby brother, Charlie,
Is snoozing in his pram
Underneath the washing line
Like a little lamb.

Clatter, clatter, crunch, crunch,
Those spiky heels go,
Crunch, scrape, clatter, clack . . .
Little does she know

That Charlie's going to wake and bawl
Any minute now
And mum is going to dash outside
And make poor Melanie howl.

But until that awful moment comes
Let little Charlie snooze
And Melanie scrape the concrete
In her mam's best shoes.

This world is full of troubles,
So let the baby snore
And Melanie go a-clattering
Half a minute more.

In Grandma's Kitchen

she lets me chop
mint leaves to make
mint sauce: I do it so fine –
chop, chop on the breadboard –
we end up with a sort of
delicious green mud;

and she lets me peel
and core bramleys for apple pies:
sometimes I trim the pastry –
trim, trim with a bright knife –
then edge it round with a neat
fork so it looks like a small
bird's been walking the rim;

then I stir the custard
yellower and yellower;
and grandad comes in smiling
from the garden – it's a nice
slow Sunday; Blackie wags
his Sunday-best tail
and we all tuck in.

A Chewy Toffee Poem

UH GLUG GLEWING GLOGGEE
GLEAT IG ALL THE GLINE

GUNGDAY
GLUESDAY
GENSDAY
GLURSDAY
GLIDAY
GLATTERDAY
GLUNDAY

GLEWING GLOGGEE'S GLUGGLY

GLORNING
GLOON
ANG GLIGHT

EGGLEGGLY GLEAGLE GLOGGEE
WIG GLAKES YR GLEEGALL GLACK

Wes

Morning Break

Andrew Flag plays football
Jane swings from the bars
Chucker Peach climbs drainpipes
Spike is seeing stars

Little Paul's a Martian
Anne walks on her toes
Ian Dump fights Kenny
Russell picks his nose

Dopey Di does hopscotch
Curly drives a train
Maddox-Brown and Lai Ching
Stuff shoes down the drain

Lisa Thin throws netballs
Ranji stands and stares
Nuttall from the first year
Shouts and spits and swears

Dick Fish fires his ray gun
Gaz has stamps to swop
Dave and Dan are robbers
Teacher is the cop

Betty Blob pulls faces
Basher falls . . . and dies
Tracey shows her knickers
Loony swallows flies

Faye sits in a puddle
Trev is eating mud
Skinhead has a nosebleed –
pints and pints of blood

Robbo Lump pings marbles
Ahmed hands out cake
What a lot of nonsense
During
        Morning
                Break

Big Aunt Flo'

Every Sunday afternoon
She visits us for tea
And weighs in somewhere between
A rhino and a flea.
　　　　　(But closer to the rhino!)

Aunt Flo' tucks into doughnuts,
Eats fruit cake by the tin.
Her stomach makes strange noises
Just like my rude friend, Flynn.
　　　　　(Sounds more like a goat, really!)

Then after tea she heads for
The best chair in the room
And crashes on the cushions
With one resounding boom.
　　　　　(You'd think a door had slammed!)

Flo' sits on knitting needles
And snaps them with a crack.
She squashes dolls and jigsaws
Behind her massive back.
　　　　　(And she doesn't feel a thing!)

But Aunt Flo' learned a lesson,
There's no doubt about that,
Last Sunday when she grabbed the chair
And sat down on our cat.
　　　　　(Big Tom, a cat with a temper!)

The beast let out a wild yell
And dug his claws in . . . deep.
Poor Flo' clutched her huge behind
And gave a massive leap.
> (She almost reached the ceiling!)

So now at Sunday teatime
Jam doughnuts going spare;
Dad winks, and asks where Flo' is
While Tom sleeps on *that* chair.
> (And he's purring, the devil!)

Menu . . . for April the First

Molten	melon
Clotted	cabbage
Battered	beans
Poached	potatoes
Coddled	carrots
Gargled	gravy
Frosted	french fries
Soggy	steak

****

Inky	ice-cream
Pickled	peaches
Curdled	custard

****

Boiled	biscuits
Curried	cheese
Barbequed	butter
Turtled	tea

Eat the lot

That's the rule

Knock it back

APRIL FOOL!

At the End of a School Day

It is the end of a school day
      and down the long drive
come bag-swinging, shouting children.
      Deafened, the sky winces.
           The sun gapes in surprise.

Suddenly the runners skid to a stop,
      stand still and stare
at a small hedgehog
      curled-up on the tarmac
           like an old, frayed cricket ball.

A girl dumps her bag, tiptoes forward
      and gingerly, so gingerly
carries the creature
      to the safety of a shady hedge.
           Then steps back, watching.

Girl, children, sky and sun
      hold their breath.
There is a silence,
      a moment to remember
           on this warm afternoon in June.

Our Miss Gill and Mr Scott

Our Miss Gill
and Mr Scott
seem to like each other
rather a lot.
His class
and our class
are always going
on trips together.
Today we climbed
Tucker's Hill
in *dreadful* weather.
      'He held her hand.'
           'Never!'
      'He did. And they kissed.'
          'No!'
It turned terribly cold.
      'I'm freezing,' said Jill.
It started to rain,
then there was sleet
and then there was snow.

At least it was warm
on the coach
and we all sang.
Arrived at the school gate
just as the bell rang.
Off we trooped home.
At the street corner
I turned
and looked back.
So did Jill.

We watched
as our Miss Gill
crossed the car park
hand in glove
with Mr Scott.
        'They are in love,'
said Jill.
Yes, they do seem
to like each other
rather a lot.

Disco Night

In the girls' cloakroom
the air gasps with *Nightfall* and *Moonwind*.
        The excitement is intense.
Everyone uses the
strawberry-flavoured lip gloss
        passed round by Geraldine Spence.

In a giggling gaggle the girls
rush to the school hall
        where the floor shines like a skating rink.
Loud music throbs and pounds.
The disco lights dazzle with flashes of
        red, mauve, yellow, green and pink.

And he's there, Dean Moffat
in a big stripy shirt
        and with gel on his spiky hair.
When the deejay yells,
'*Go grab 'em, girls!*'
        Lisa drags him, protesting, off his chair.

                *   *   *

Next morning, Lisa is at the centre
of a playground huddle of girls.
        '*What happened?*' '*Tell us!*' '*Own up!*'
Lisa smiles. '*I think he loves me,*'
she says, '*and I bet he marries me*
        when we're grown up!'

The Meadow in Midsummer

Immobilized by June heat
the chestnut trees are calm cathedrals
    of bough and leaf.
In their deep shade
half-hidden horses
    seek cool relief.

The pond's azure eye
gazes amazed at the gold coin
    dazzling the sky
as, barefoot amidst buttercups,
we cross the meadow,
    slowly pass by.

39

Faraway Places

Faraway places
     are calling to me
faraway places
     over land
          over sea
snow-mufflered Moscow
     the frozen South Pole
east to Kyoto
     and Hong Kong and Seoul
dripping wet jungles
     vast African plain
north to Yakutsk by
     Siberian train
Matterhorn mountain
     adrift on the Med
nights in the desert
     with stars overhead
trekking the Outback
     exploring Vietnam
up the Grand Canyon
     to Grand Coulee Dam
Outer Mongolia
     and Island Magee
faraway places
     are calling to me
Lake Titicaca
     Belize and Bel-Air
Kabul, Kurdistan
     and County Kildare.

Faraway places
    are calling to me
faraway places
    over land
        over sea
faraway places
    are calling me there
the sun on my face
    the wind in my hair
faraway places
    faraway places
are calling me
    calling me
        calling me
            there.

How to Reach the Sun . . .
on a Piece of Paper

Take a sheet of paper
and fold it,
and fold it again,
and again, and again.
By the 6th fold
it is 1 centimetre thick.

By the 11th fold
it will be 32 centimetres thick,
and by the 15th fold
– 5 metres.

At the 20th fold
it measures 160 metres.
At the 24th fold,
– 2.5 kilometres
and by fold 30
is 160 kilometres high.

At the 35th fold
– 5000 kilometres.
At the 43rd fold
it will reach to the moon.

And by fold 52
will stretch from here
      to the sun!
Take a sheet of paper.
Go on.
      Try it!

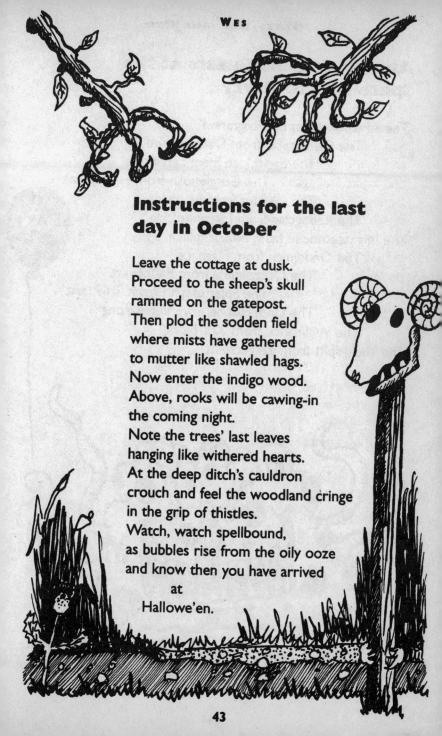

Instructions for the last day in October

Leave the cottage at dusk.
Proceed to the sheep's skull
rammed on the gatepost.
Then plod the sodden field
where mists have gathered
to mutter like shawled hags.
Now enter the indigo wood.
Above, rooks will be cawing-in
the coming night.
Note the trees' last leaves
hanging like withered hearts.
At the deep ditch's cauldron
crouch and feel the woodland cringe
in the grip of thistles.
Watch, watch spellbound,
as bubbles rise from the oily ooze
and know then you have arrived
        at
        Hallowe'en.

Announcing the Guests at the Space Beasts' Party

'The Araspew from Bashergrannd'
   'The Cakkaspoo from Danglebannd'
      'The Eggisplosh from Ferrintole'
         'The Gurglenosh from Hiccupole'
      'The Inkiblag from Jupitickle'
      'The Kellogclag from Lamandpickle'
'The Mighteemoose from Nosuchplace'
   'The Orridjuice from Piggiface'
      'The Quizziknutt from Radishratt'
         'The Splattersplut from Trikkicatt'
      'The Underpance from Verristrong'
   'The Willidance from Xrayblong'
'The Yuckyspitt from Ziggersplitt'

WES

<u>A</u> Who'<u>Z</u> Who of the Horrible House

Inside
the
Horrible
House
there is
an awful aquamarine apparition abseiling
a bug-eyed beige bogeyman boxing
a cackling crimson cockroach creeping
a disgusting damson Dracula dancing
an eerie emerald elf electrocuting
a floppy flame Frankenstein fencing
a grotty green ghost groaning
a haunting hazel hag hammering
an insane indigo imp ice-screaming
a jittery jade jackal juggling
a kinky khaki king knitting
a loony lime leprechaun lasooing
a monocled maroon madman marching
a nightmarish navy nastie nipping
an outrageous orange ogre oozing
a phoolish purple phantom phoning
a quadruple quicksilver quagga quaking
a revolting red rattlesnake rock 'n' rolling
a spotty scarlet spectre spitting
a terrible turquoise troll trampolining
an ugly umber uncle umpiring
a violent violet vampire vibrating
a whiskery white werewolf windsurfing
an eXcitable xanthic eXoskeleton eXploding
a yucky yellow yak yelling
a zitty zinc zombie zapping
inside
the
Horrible
House!

The House on the Hill

It was built years ago
by someone quite manic
and sends those who go there
away in blind panic.
They tell tales of horrors
that can injure or kill
designed by the madman
who lived on the hill.

If you visit the House on the Hill for a dare
remember my words . . .

'There are dangers. Beware!'

The piano's white teeth
when you plonk out a note
will bite off your fingers
then reach for your throat.
The living-room curtains
– long, heavy and black –
will wrap you in cobwebs
if you're slow to step back.

If you visit the House on the Hill for a dare
remember my words . . .

'There are dangers. Beware!'

46

The fridge in the kitchen
has a self-closing door.
If it locks you inside
then you're ice-cubes . . . for sure.
The steps to the cellar
are littered with bones,
and up from the darkness
drift creakings and groans.

If you visit the House on the Hill for a dare
remember my words . . .

'There are dangers. Beware!'

Turn on the hot tap
and the bathroom will flood
not with gallons of water
but litres of blood.
The rocking-chair's arms
can squeeze you to death;
a waste of time shouting
as you run . . . out . . . of . . . breath.

Don't say you weren't warned or told to take care
when you entered the House on the Hill . . .

for a dare.

In the Castle of Gloom

Oh,
it's cold,
it's as cold as a tomb,
and
it's dark
as a windowless room
in
the Castle,
the Castle of Gloom.

(meet your dooooom)

No sun through the shutters.
No candle flame gutters.
No log embers glimmer.
No silver plates shimmer.
No lamps in the hall.
No brands on the wall.
No moonbeams at night.
No starshine.
No light.

Oh,
it's cold,
it's as cold as a tomb,
and
it's dark
as a windowless room
in
the Castle,
the Castle of Gloom.

(meet your dooooooooooom)

Footballers in the Park

December. Wet Saturday in the park.
It's late afternoon and it's growing dark

as a bevy of boys play their football game.
Most wear baggy shorts. One goalie's lame.

Posts are old jerseys and hand-me-down coats;
the boys' boots are bulky as rowing boats.

Leather ball's sodden and heavy with mud.
It thumps a boy's face with a squelchy thud

and blood dribbles down from a nose struck numb:
a fat lad stunningly skids on his bum.

One boy shivers in his 'Wednesday' shirt,
the collar's ripped and he's plastered with dirt.

The game rattles on; chill drizzle sets in.
The wind in the trees makes a Cup Final din.

Distantly, lights shine on the wet street
unnoticed by boys whose thundering feet

are playing the game. But the hour grows late.
Here comes the park keeper to padlock the gate.

And the year is 1948.

Exploring the Deserted Mansion

In the hall . . .
>cobwebs hang from the crumbling ceiling,
>antlered hatstand is carved from oak,
>turquoise carpet's all tattered and torn,
>and dust in the air makes you choke.
>>Chilly,
>>icy house.
>>Dank,
>>deserted place.

In the kitchen . . .
>two tarnished taps drip brackish water,
>the stale loaf's grown a coat of mould,
>a strong stench seeps up from the drains,
>and the radiators feel stone cold.
>>Foul and
>>fusty house.
>>Damp,
>>deserted place.

On the landing . . .
>a headless, rusty suit of armour,
>the old oil portrait's mint eyes glare,
>shattered mirror in its silver frame,
>and rat bones on the rocking-chair.
>>Creaky,
>>echoing house.
>>Dark,
>>deserted place.

In the bedroom . . .
>   a tousled bed with blood-stained pillow,
>   rent curtains billow in the breeze,
>   black cockroach scuttles over floorboards,
>   and a sudden scream makes you freeze.
>>   Pale and
>>   faded house.
>>   Dim,
>>   deserted place.

Up in the attic . . .
>   a white wedding gown's a nest for mice,
>   there's Santa's sack for Christmas Eve,
>   brown bats hang from the wood-wormed beams,
>   the trapdoor's jammed . . .
>>>   when you try to leave!
>>   Grim and
>>   creepy house.
>>   Dead,
>>   deserted place.

Afraid of the Dark?

Not me. I like the dark
and the way it closes round me
like a big, friendly duvet
after they've said, 'Goodnight,
sleep tight, watch the bugs don't bite!'
and switched off my bedroom light.
I lie in the darkness
listening to sounds outside.
Someone shouts. A dog barks.
A motorbike roars past, changes gear,
and fades away into the distance,
                    and slowly I drop . . .
                                        off . . .
                                            to . . .
                                                sleep . . .

It's then I grow scared.
The nightmares come and overwhelm me.
In one I'm clinging
to the mane of a runaway horse.
We jump a ditch, leap a thick hedge,
but at the stone wall I'm thrown.
I fall . . . fall . . . fall . . .
In another I'm alone
at the wheel of a racing car.
The brakes fail. The car speeds
towards a deep and gloomy lake.
        Splash! And I go
                            down . . .
                                down . . .
                                    down . . .

I wake, sweating with fright.
My bedside clock shows 2.00 a.m.
The house is silent as the grave.
I stare into the thrumming night
and the darkness calms me.
The nightmares shrink and sink
into the centre of my skull.
I lie there, the darkness soothing
. . . like Mum's hand on my forehead
when I was ill with the flu,
and quietly, gently,
     and slowly I drop . . .

            off . . .

               to . . .

                   sleep . . .

Oh, No You Don't!

For a Christmas treat
Dad took me and four friends
to see *Cinderella* in town.
There was loud music, excitement,
and sweets in crackly paper
when the theatre lights went down.

During the interval
we tucked into choc ices
and cans of fizzy drink.
On stage, mice and a pumpkin
turned into a coach and horses
quicker than you could blink.

Then, wearing wigs of fluorescent red,
the Ugly Sisters waddled on.
Their noses were livid blue.
'Oh, no you don't!' they shouted.
'Oh, yes we do!' we replied. 'OH, NO YOU DON'T!'
'OH, YES WE DO! OH, YES WE DO!'

When it was over we filed out
and squashed into the back seat
of Dad's big, old car.
Jolting, we headed home.
Overhead the sky was jet black.
'There's the Plough!' 'And the North Star!'

Suddenly, my friend said,
*'Jane's feeling ill.
I think she's going to be sick!'*
'Oh, no she's isn't,' Dad muttered grimly.
'Oh, yes she is!' we chorused.
'Stop the car! Quick! QUICK!'

UGGGGH!

The Tunneller

At number 42
there's a hawthorn perimeter hedge
and the front gate is topped
with strands of barbed wire.
The mad Major lives there,
a septuagenarian ex-soldier
with military moustache
and a broom-handle-straight back.

On a mission,
in the last War, he parachuted into Germany,
was captured, and then held
in a prison camp: Stalag number 39.
He tunnelled out, escaped to England.
His true story is printed in a book
I found at the library:
Spies of the Second World War.

Yesterday,
at dusk, I hid in his long back garden
and spied on the Major
as he passed the old air-raid shelter
and marched into his garden shed.
He was dressed in black –
trousers, sweater, and woolly Balaclava.
Dirt streaks disguised his face.

I sneaked up
and through the cobwebby window
watched as the Major removed floorboards,
then lowered himself into a hole
and . . . disappeared!
He was tunnelling again,
digging beneath his back garden,
tunnelling towards the perimeter hedge.

An hour later
he emerged furtively from the shed
lugging a heavy sack
and I saw him scatter damp soil
between his rhubarb and cauliflowers.
Night after night he's at it,
secretly tunnelling his way to freedom,
trying to escape from Stalag number 42.

He Loves Me, He Loves Me Not . . .

It's hot, sweltering, as children
spill from the school at lunchtime
and spread across the field.
  Friday: Fry-day. Sun-high noon.
Today it's the thirtieth day
  of a heatwave June.

With legs splayed wide
three girls sit and pick daisies.
They must endure Sports Day heats
  all that long, hot afternoon.
For them the summer holidays
  just can't arrive too soon.

        He loves me
        he loves me not
        he loves me
        he loves me not
        he loves me . . .

It's a massacre.
Around the girls
lie picked daisies by the score,
  dying in the sun-stunned air.
The sky's albino eye unblinking:
  a fierce, fixing glare.

The girls chant lazily
dreaming who'll be the one
to get lucky with Richard,
  the boy with the flame-red hair.
Will it be Francesca, or Anne-Marie,
  or Claire?

  He loves me
  he loves me not
  he loves me
  he loves me not
  he loves me . . .

Football!

Football! *Football!*
The boys want the entire playground
and we're left squashed
against the broken fence.
Why don't the teachers stop them?
    Why?
Haven't they got *any* sense?

My friend Anna
ran across the tarmac. Smack!
Got the football right on her nose.
Blood all over her face.
Why don't the teachers do something?
    Why?
It's a disgrace, *a disgrace!*

Those boys . . . I mean
they're like hooligans.
CHEL-SEA! CHEL-SEA! they chant
morning, noon and night.
The teacher on duty does . . . nothing.
    Why?
It's just . . . it's just not right!

We complain bitterly
but the duty teacher says,
'*Go and see the Head. He's in charge.*'
Him! He's useless! YOU-ESS-LESS!
When we ask him to ban football
    why,
oh why, can't he just say 'Yes"?

Pete

Teabag

I'd like to be a teabag,
And stay at home all day
and talk to other teabags
in a teabag sort of way.

I'd love to be a teabag,
And lie in a little box
and never have to wash my face
or change my dirty socks.

I'd like to be a Tetley bag,
An Earl Grey one perhaps,
and doze all day and lie around
with Earl Grey kind of chaps.

I wouldn't have to do a thing,
No homework, jobs or chores –
just lie inside a comfy box
of teabags and their snores.

I wouldn't have to do exams,
I needn't tidy rooms,
or sweep the floor, or feed the cat
or wash up all the spoons.

I wouldn't have to do a thing –
A life of bliss, you see . . .
except that once in all my life

I'd make a cup of tea.

My Mum

My mum was a mince pie of a mum.
A 'doyouwantabiscuitwithyourtea?'
kind of mum.
A roast potato
    brown gravy
    crackle on the pork
    Yorkshire pud
kind of lady.
She was a
    houseful of everyone
    polish the brass
    whiten the step
    rush to the shops
    bucket and mops
kind of lady.

A – 'hello dear'
    always near
    hurry scurry
'Oh, don't worry . . .'
kind of mum.

She collected –
   old people
   funny stories
   and other people's children.

She called everyone by an invented name
and was a champion
                    bus waiter
                    queuer
                    visitor
                    laugher
            and Nutall Mint sucker.

She was someone
who
would give anyone
her last mint.

Chicken-spots

I've got these really itchy spots,
they're climbing on my tummy.
They're on my head,
they're on my tail
and it isn't very funny.
They came to see me yesterday
– a few the day before
fifty on my bottom
and twenty on my jaw.

I've got a prize one on my toe,
a dozen on my knee
and now they're on my thingy
    – I think there's thirty-three!

I count them every evening
I give them names like Fred –
    Charlie, Di and Daisy . . .
    Chunky, Tom and Ted.

They're really awful spotties
they drive me itchy mad
the sort of itchy itches
I wish I never had.
Nobby's worst at itching
Lizzie's awful too
and – if you come to see me
I'll give a few to you . . .
 I'll give you Di and Daisy
 I'll give you Jane and Ted,
 a bucket full of itchers
 to take home to your bed . . .
 You can give them to your sister
 I don't care what you do.
 Give them to a teacher
 or send them to the zoo.
 I don't mind where you take 'em
 I don't care where they go . . .
 stick them up the chimney
 or in the baby's po.
 Take them to a farmyard.
 Find a chicken pen
 and say that they're a present

 with love

 from me

 to Them!

Little Arnold and the Dodo

One day
Little Arnold found a Dodo.
He found it in the park,
Right behind some bushes
Where it was very dark.

Little Arnold took the Dodo
And put it in a box,
And kept it in the cellar
In a nest he made of socks.

Little Arnold loved the Dodo
He fed it every day,
And told it Dodo stories
So it wouldn't go away.

He told it tales of wonder
He told it tales of life
Then he went and searched for others –
All Dodos need a wife.

He searched for many hours,
He sought both high and low.
Then saw one in the bushes
Where Dodos like to go.

'Oh come here, Mrs Dodo,'
Good Little Arnold cried,
'I have a Dodo man for you,'
And Mrs Dodo sighed.

So now they have a Dodo nest,
Mr Dodo has a bride.
They lay a Dodo egg a day,
and Arnold has it —

                fried.

Big·Billy

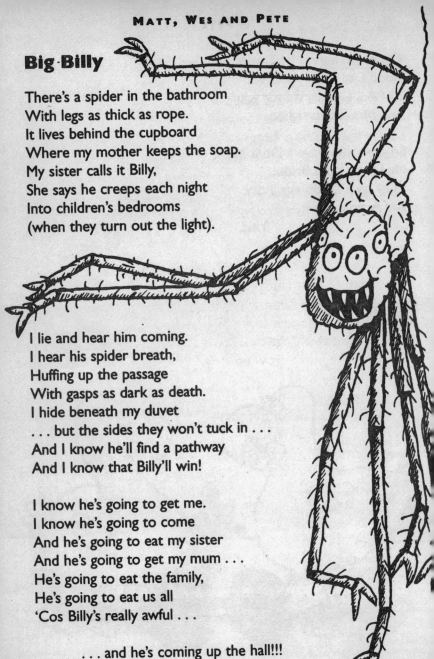

There's a spider in the bathroom
With legs as thick as rope.
It lives behind the cupboard
Where my mother keeps the soap.
My sister calls it Billy,
She says he creeps each night
Into children's bedrooms
(when they turn out the light).

I lie and hear him coming.
I hear his spider breath,
Huffing up the passage
With gasps as dark as death.
I hide beneath my duvet
. . . but the sides they won't tuck in . . .
And I know he'll find a pathway
And I know that Billy'll win!

I know he's going to get me.
I know he's going to come
And he's going to eat my sister
And he's going to get my mum . . .
He's going to eat the family,
He's going to eat us all
'Cos Billy's really awful . . .

. . . and he's coming up the hall!!!

Tadpoles

Said the tadpole to the tadpole
as they tadpoled round their jar
I don't want to be a froggy
I don't want to grow that far.
I'm happy as I am now
black blob and little tail,
I don't want to be a froggy
or a toady
or a whale.

I just want to be a taddy
I want to stay the same,
I liked being frogspawn
I didn't want to change . . .
Oh, why've I got to grow up
and be an ugly toad,
creep around in ditches
 – and get squashed in the road.
I'd like to stay a taddy
stay the same for life.
This jar can be my palace . . .

and you can be my wife.

DYING DOG

DESERT SUN

SPIES A PUDDLE

ONLY ONE

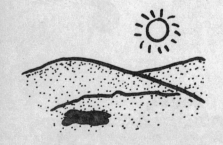

LAPS THE PUDDLE

 TRAVELS ON

BARKS A 'THANK YOU'

 PUDDLE
GONE

Happy Dogday

Today
Is our dog's birthday.

It's Happydogdayday.
Sixteen years of panting
And sixteen years of play.

Sixteen years of dogtime.
Sixteen years of barks
– eating smelly dog food
And making muddy marks.

It's a hundred years of our time.
It's a hundred human years
– of digging in the garden
and scratching itchy ears.
It's a hundred years of living rooms
(he never goes upstairs)
and dropping hairy whiskers
and being pushed off chairs . . .

It's a hundred years of being with us
A hundred years of Dad,
and a hundred years of my sister
(that must be really bad!)

So:
No wonder he looks really old
No wonder he is grey
And cannot hear
Or jump
Or catch
Or even run away . . .
No wonder that he sleeps all day,
No wonder that he's fat
And only dreams of catching things
and chasing neighbours' cats . . .

So fight your fights
In dogdream nights
Deep within your bed . . .

today's your day
and we all say . . .

HAPPY BIRTHDAY FRED

Miss Hubbard

She's at the window again!
Bug eyed,
Dressing gowned, and grey.
'See her!'
squeal the Brownie Pack returning from St Johns
'See her!'
chorus the boys returning from nowheremuch.
And there she stares –
Tall
and gaunt
and hair unpinned . . .

          staring
          staring
          staring
staring beyond the silver slates
          of Stanley Street
          of Wilmer Way
          and distant Arnos Grove.

Head tilted,
as if by mechanical device
Unmoving,
and unflinching at the handful of gravel
thrown at her window by the captain of the
Boys' Brigade . . .
          Always staring.
          Never watching,
          Always staring.
          Staring at her moon.
'Miss Hubbard's moon starin'!' echoed the
          Bunyan boys from 43.

And the children gathered
And the pink fingers pointed,
And the gravel rattled.
And still she stared.
And from the houses the grown ups came —
Nodding
And whispering
And pointing . . .

and murmuring wise
things amongst themselves —
To lead the children away.
Later that year they also led Miss Hubbard away.
Slowly
And kindly
For staring at the moon.

Where Do All the Teachers Go?

Where do all the teachers go
When it's 4 o'clock?
Do they live in houses
And do they wash their socks?

Do they wear pyjamas
And do they watch TV?
And do they pick their noses
The same as you and me?

Do they live with other people?
Have they mums and dads?
And were they ever children?
And were they ever bad?

Did they ever, never spell right?
Did they ever makes mistakes?
Were they punished in the corner
If they pinched the chocolate flakes?

Did they ever lose their hymn books?
Did they ever leave their greens?
Did they scribble on the desk tops?
Did they wear old dirty jeans?

I'll follow one back home today
I'll find out what they do
Then I'll put it in a poem
That they can read to you.

A Sembly

Teachers tall as pencils
standing by the wall.
Infants bright as Leggo
filling half the hall.
Juniors full of whispers,
fourth years full of cheek –

A sembly's really awful,
And we have them every week.

Nativity Play

This year . . .
This year can I be Herod?
This year, can I be him?
A wiseman
or a Joseph?
An inn man
or a king?

This year . . .
can I be famous?
This year, can I be best?
Bear a crown of silver
and wear a golden vest?

This year . . .
can I be starlight?
This year, can I stand out?

. . . feel the swish of curtains
and hear the front row shout
'Hurrah' for good old Ronny
he brings a gift of gold
head afire with tinsel
'The Greatest Story Told . . .'
'Hurrah for good old Herod!'
and shepherds from afar.

So –
don't make me a palm tree.
And can I be –

a Star.

Miss Spelling

Our teacher's called Miss Spelling,

she's a sort of spelling freak –

spellings every morning

spellings every week –

      beak
      leek
      teak

   It's spellings for our homework

   It's spellings on the wall

   It's spellings in our workbooks

   and it's spellings in the hall.

Miss Spelling's spelling crazy

   spells spellings every day
   when
     and where
      and whatsit . . .

          there
           and then
            and they . . .'

We've never written stories,

I don't think we ever could,

But when it comes to spelling

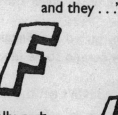

Our teacher's really ~~god.~~ good

Sp. See me.
Miss Spelling

A Girl I Know . . .

A girl I know called Emma Rose
stuck her finger up her nose
in class
in story
silent reading
morning prayers
and even singing.
She did it on the trip to France
and halfway through the Maypole dance,
She did it in the Christmas play
on the stage on full display . . .

She did it by the king of kings
right behind the angel wings!

'Pull it down!'
the teachers muttered . . .
whilst parents wept
and shepherds spluttered.

She coughed, she blew
she tried to suck
but Emma's finger now was stuck!

They pulled the curtain
they served some tea . . .

but couldn't get the finger free

But then a wiseman had a thought

and pushed some pepper up her snort

a sniff, a tickle,
then a shout

and Emma's finger flew right out.

The palm trees cheered,
the donkeys brayed,
governors clapped
and music played . . .

Hurrah for Emma!

Christmas too!

But what a silly thing

to do.

Rotten Reader

I'm a really rotten reader
the worst in all the class,
the sort of rotten reader
that makes you want to laugh.

I'm last in all the readin' tests,
my score's not on the page
and when I read to teacher
she gets in such a rage.

She says I cannot form my words
She says I can't build up
and that I don't know phonics
– and don't know c-a-t from k-u-p.

They say that I'm dyslectic
(that's a word they've just found out)
. . . but when I get some Plasticine
I know what that's about.

I make these scary monsters
I draw these secret lands
and get my hair all sticky
and paint on all me hands.

I make these super models,
I build these smashing towers
that reach up to the ceiling
and take me hours and hours.

I paint these lovely pictures
in thick green drippy paint
that gets all on the carpets
and makes the cleaners faint.

I build great magic forests,
weave bushes out of string
and paint pink panderellos
and birds that really sing.

I play my world of real believe
I play it every day
and teachers stand and watch me
but don't know what to say.

They give me diagnostic tests,
they try out reading schemes,
but none of them will ever know
the colour of my dreams.

Queenie

Our hamster died at playtime
Beside her silver wheel,
Closed her eyes for ever
(she ate some orange peel.)
She closed her eyes for ever
She twitched her nose no more,
A sleeping looking hamster
(except she couldn't snore) . . .

Yes,
Queenie died at playtime
We gathered round her cage
and retold hamster stories
(and argued of her age.)
We recalled bitten fingers,
Escapes and hunts galore
And twenty-seven babies
 – adventures by the score.

The day inside the cooker
The week beneath the floor
And getting in the powder paint
And gnawing through the door.

We swapped our hamster stories
(we made some up as well)
Then heard the teachers coming
(we never heard the bell.)

'The hamster's dead, Miss Simmonds,
The hamster's just gone dead –
And have a look, Miss Simmonds –
a fly's got on its head.'

Miss Simmonds ordered silence
Demanded – 'Look this way . . .
It's half past ten, and Thursday,
And time for work not play.'

Breaking Friends With Sharon

I've broken friends with Sharon
she's broken friends with me.
I told her I don't like her,
she said she don't like me.
Sharon's really silly
Sharon never shares,
snatches pens and peanuts
Sharon even swears.

Sharon – we don't play now
Sharon plays with Jo
and I don't go to Brownies -
— not if Sharon goes.

She told Miss Andrews of me,
she told my sister lies.
I think her new coat's awful
her face,
          her smile
                    and eyes.
I think she's really nasty,
I'd love to see her go,
but one thing's really awkward . . .
what if she says —

                    'Hello'

School Trip

I saw a man in a cardboard box
I saw a lady too,
Her head was wrapped in paper,
She only had one shoe.
We went and saw where Nelson is
We visited St Paul's,
We visited the Palace
and we climbed the city walls.

We saw the Tower Bridge open,
We went and saw Big Ben

     . . . but I remember ladies
        and boxes full of men.

Blocked Drain

The drain is blocked with a football sock
(and Keep Away said Sir).
The water's murky, the water's dirty
(and Keep Away said Sir).
It's deep and slimy, brown and grimy,
(so Don't go Near, said Sir).
But Lizzie did,
she did a dare
she jumped it right across

(almost),
and floated sticks
and threw some bricks
then pushed at Mary Cross.
Well – Mary Cross got angry,
she spat a bit of spit,
Tony Rogers dodged it –
but poor Ben Jones got hit!
He ran and told his brother
and he told Rory Cray
who went and told Big Dawkins
and he fetched Porky Day.

. . .

Porky Day came runnin'
then tripped on Tigger's boot,
he fell against his sister
and she knocked Sally Root.

. . .

Sally Root went flying
A S-P-L-A-S-H
as black as jet . . .
Her dress awash with water
Her knickers soaking wet.
The juniors all went silent,
the infants ran away,
tears plopped into the puddle
then up came Porky Day . . .
He laughed and splashed her even more.
He poked her with a stick
and flipped a lot of muddy stuff
that smelt like puddle sick.
He laughed and kicked a great big splash
He went to do some more
          then –
came a mighty thunder
a sort of puddle roar.

The puddle rose
a mushroom form
of stinking sock and slime
ripples brown as cocoa
a smell like farmyard swine.
It hovered over Porky Day
his eyes were filled with dread
the puddle gave a tremble
then jumped right on his head!

Poor Porky lay awash with slosh
an infant called 'Hooray' . . .

            the puddle grinned
                    and gurgled
                            then quietly
                                    ran away.

King of the Toilets

Maurice was King of the toilets.
The ones by the wall – by the shed,
He ruled with the power and conviction
Of a king with a crown on his head.

He entered them FIRST every morning
He'd sit on the wall by the gate
And wait for the grumpy schoolkeeper
To unlock them – at twenty past eight.

Then he'd rush in with great shouts of triumph
And he'd slam all the doors one by one
And he'd climb on the caretaker's cupboards
And he'd pull all the chains just for fun.

He'd swing on the pipes by the cistern,
he'd leap from the top of the doors,
And he'd frighten the new little infants
With bellows and yellings and roars.

He always ate lunch in the toilets,
He'd sit with his food on the floor,
And check who was coming (or going)
And kick at the catch on their door.

He once burst the pipe by the outflow,
By climbing right up on the tank,
And flooded the lower school library,
With water that gushed out and stank.

He once jammed the door on the end one
With five juniors stuck fast inside,
And bombed them with piles of old comics
Whilst they struggled and shouted and cried.

He was useless in class, and at lessons.
He couldn't do hardly a thing —
But when he was out in the toilets,

THEN MAURICE THE USELESS WAS KING!

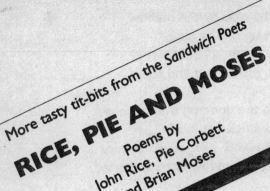

More tasty tit-bits from the Sandwich Poets

RICE, PIE AND MOSES

Poems by
John Rice, Pie Corbett
and Brian Moses

Other Macmillan Children's Poetry Books
you won't be able to resist . . .

DRACULA'S AUNTIE RUTHLESS
And Other Petrifying Poems

SNOGGERS!
Slap 'n' Tickle Poems

'ERE WE GO!
Football Poems

DOIN MI ED IN
Rap Poems